**From Lynn and Laurie,**

As a society, we have unintentionally kept children from participating fully in a healthy grieving process. In our efforts to protect them, we inadvertently do them a great disservice. Children need not be the neglected mourners that they so often are.

The many feelings of grief can become a maze of confusion unless broken down into small parts that can be easily understood. Nationally known grief counselor Dr. Alan Wolfelt defines this process as "activities associated with thinking through the loss, facing its realities, expressing the feelings... and becoming reinvolved with life." *A Keepsake Book of Special Memories: Helping Children Heal from Loss* guides children, one step at a time, through this complex process in a way that is safe and nurturing.

This keepsake book has been created to help children express their grief, enabling them to cope with the death of someone close. Designed specifically for children, the book encourages self-expression using a variety of techniques comfortable to children—drawing, writing, storytelling, collage making, coloring, etc. The work involved in completing the book is therapeutic and instrumental in the healing process. The book, when finished, becomes an everlasting keepsake.

If we listen patiently, children will teach us about their grief. Children who have the ability to grieve are more likely to become adults better prepared for life's challenges. *A Keepsake Book of Special Memories* brings into focus a vision where all children can grieve in a new and healthy way.

*Adult may remove this page and keep for reference.*

# How to Use This Book

## Who Should Use This Book

A *Keepsake Book of Special Memories* is designed to be completed by a child (ages 4–12) with the help of a supportive adult—a parent, family member, friend, teacher, or counselor. Older children may want to do some of the book by themselves. Honor their need for privacy, but continue to offer support, monitor their progress, maintain communication, and encourage the sharing of feelings.

## Getting Started

Before you begin, carefully read through the Guide to Contents. It briefly describes the purpose of each section and will help you to choose an appropriate starting point for your unique situation. Do not feel compelled to begin at the beginning or work your way through from front the back. *Children feel safer completing the book slowly, no more than one, two, or three pages at a time.* As the adult, take your cues from the child. Be ready to talk about death. Be ready to listen. Remembering and sharing breaks the isolation and validates the child's loss. Taking the time now will spare much unnecessary pain in the future.

You will need patience and a warm heart. You may use a variety of materials to create a memory book: photographs, pencils, pens, crayons, glue stick, scissors, or old magazines. It may be a good idea to have these materials ready before starting on the book. Turn off the phone and ask that you not be interrupted while working.

## Children's Needs

If the child is too young to write, or feels uncomfortable completing the book, you may need to ask the questions and record the responses. It is important to be aware of symptoms such as nervousness, fear, anger, change of appetite and sleeping patterns, low self–esteem, and the inability to enjoy life over an extended period of time. Do not hesitate to seek professional help if you feel it is needed.

*Adult may remove this page and keep for reference.*

# Guide to Contents

*Adult may remove this page and keep for reference.*

# Additional Resources

**Children's Books: Ages Four through Twelve**

*I Miss You*, by Pat Thomas
(Barron's Educational Series, Inc. 2000)

*When Dinosaurs Die*, by Laurie Krasney Brown & Marc Brown
(Little, Brown & Company, 2009)

*The Goodbye Boat*, by Mary Joslin
(Eerdmans Publishing Company, 1998)

*Sad Isn't Bad*, by Michaelene Mundy
(Abbey Press, 1998)

*The Great Change*, by White Deer of Autumn
(Beyond Words Publishing, Inc. 1992)

*The Tenth Good Thing About Barney*, by Judith Viorst
(Simon & Schuster, 1971)

*How I Feel: A Coloring Book*, by Dr. Alan Wolfelt
(Companion Press, 1996)

**Books for Any Age, Even Adults**

*Fall Of Freddie The Leaf*, by Leo Buscaglia
(Slack, Inc., 1982)

*The Velveteen Rabbit*, by Marjery Williams
(Harper, 2004)

**Books for Any Age, Even Adults,** Continued

*Aarvy Aardvark Finds Hope*, by Donna O'Toole
(Compassion Press, 1988)

*Lifetimes*, by Bryan Mellonie & Robert Ingpen
(Random House, 1983)

*Tear Soup*, by Pat Schweibert & Chuck DeKlyen
(Grief Watch, 1999)

**Books for Adults and Professionals**

*Helping Children Grieve and Grow*, by Donna O'Toole
with Jerre Corey (Compassion Press, 1998)

*The Journey Through Grief And Loss*, by Robert Zucker
(St. Martins Press, 2009)

*How Do We Tell The Children*, by Daniel Schaefer
& Christine Lyons (Newmarket Press, 2010)

**Compassion Press** · ©2012
www.compassionbooks.com · 800.970.4220
*7036 State Hwy. 80 South · Burnsville, NC 28714*

*Adult may remove this page and keep for reference.*

# My Special Memories

of _____
*name*

Love_____

# Memory Photos

Here are some picture memories

of _____
<small>*name*</small>

*Glue photo(s) here*

Today is _____
<small>*date*</small>

2

# Dates

_____ was born
*name*

_____
*day*

_____
*month*

_____
*year*

_____ died on
*name*

_____
*day*

_____
*month*

_____
*year*

# My Feelings

I was _____ years old
          *number*

when _____ died.
     *name*

I was _____
      *activity*

_____

when I learned _____ had died.
             *name*

I was told by _____
         *name*

that _____
    *what happened*

I felt . . .
   *write or draw*

# Feeling Sad

I feel so sad about _____ dying. It is OK to cry and
*name*
feel sad. It will help my sadness to go away if I cry!

If I want to laugh and have fun, that is OK too.

What do I feel like doing now?

_____

_____

_____

_____

_____

_____

_____

_____

# Body Awareness

When I feel very sad my body might feel different too.

Listen to your body. Look at the picture on the next page.
Write how your body feels.

_____

_____

_____

I can take good care of my body. These are some of the different
ways I can take care of myself.

_____

_____

_____

_____

## Show where your body bothers you.

heart hurts?

7

# Feeling Angry

I may have angry feelings after someone I love dies.

When do I feel angry?_____

_____

_____

_____

Things that make me feel angry. _____

_____

_____

_____

## Things you can do when you feel angry...

Talk about it  •  Cry or laugh  •  Throw something soft against a wall and say your feelings out loud  •  Hit a pillow... hit a punching bag  •  Yell or shout  •  Play your favorite sport  •  Make two fists... pull your shoulders up to touch your ears and let go  •  Kick a ball  •  Take a crayon and paper and scribble very hard saying out loud what you are angry about  •  Hug a stuffed animal  •  Write your feelings down

What does it look like to feel angry? Draw a picture or make a collage.

# Grief

Grief is a very sad feeling we have when someone we love has left us.

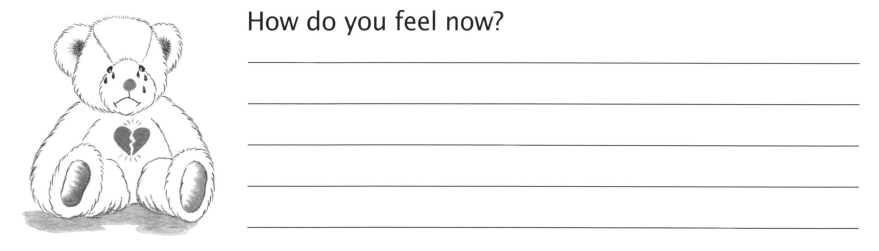

How do you feel now?

_____

_____

_____

_____

Draw a picture of what your own grief feels like.

# Saying Goodbye

Our family had different kinds of feelings
when_____died.
<sub>name</sub>

How did others in your family feel?_____

_____

_____

We shared our loss together. Share some of the ways your
family said goodbye._____

_____

_____

_____

I wonder if . . .

11

# Mixed-up Feelings

Sometimes I feel mixed-up inside. My feelings are OK.

Circle the feelings you have now, or add your own feelings; come back at another time and put a square around different feelings.

joyful, angry, _____, quiet, hopeful, confused, lonely, happy, alone, _____, proud, tense, numb, relieved, caring, anxious, nervous, miserable, guilty, playful, loveable, ashamed, relaxed, loved, depressed, shocked, dreamy, sad, painful, overwhelmed, courageous, eager, weird, angry, empty, hungry, terrified, tired, silly, peaceful, different, jealous, fearful

It's okay to talk about your feelings with your family or a friend who cares. Write the names of some people who you can share your feelings with._____

_____

# Feeling Upset

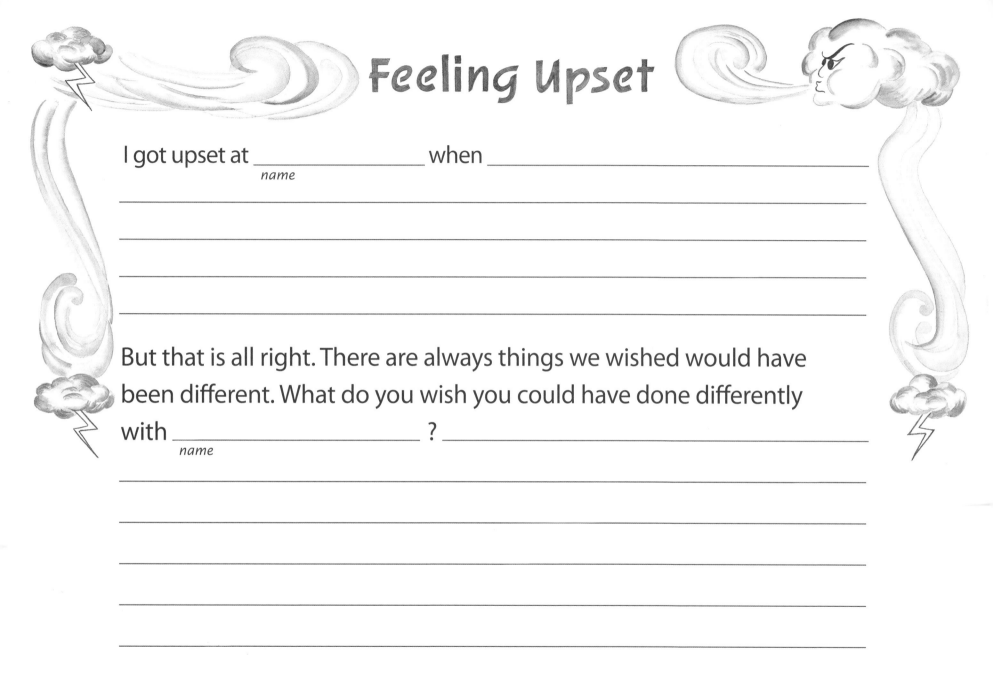

I got upset at _____ when _____
                    *name*

_____

_____

_____

_____

But that is all right. There are always things we wished would have
been different. What do you wish you could have done differently
with _____ ? _____
        *name*

_____

_____

_____

_____

_____

# Friends

At school I felt _____

_____

_____

My friends _____

_____

_____

_____

I wish my friends would _____

_____

_____

_____

14

# My Memories

Our special feelings for one another will never go away.

These are ways I will always remember _____
*name*

_____

_____

_____

_____

_____

_____

_____

_____

These special memories
will always be there to
treasure.

*Add more later if you remember more*

15

# My Memories

_____ loved to eat _____
*name*

_____

_____ lived _____
*name*                      *describe where*

_____

Favorite things_____liked to do_____
                *name*

_____

_____

_____

_____

I remember_____would like to wear_____
           *name*

_____

when_____

_____

# My Memories

The things I remember and will miss most are . . .

_____

_____

_____

I won't miss _____

_____

_____

Since _____ died I sometimes worry that _____
       _name_

_____

_____

_____

_____

_____

17

# My Memories

Some of the funny times we shared together were _____

_____

 _____

_____

_____

Draw pictures or glue photo(s) here

# My Memories

Some of the things _____ taught me were _____
                              *name*

_____

_____

_____

I would tell _____ that it was fun when we _____
                        *name*

_____

_____

_____

We laughed when _____

_____

_____

# Feeling Afraid and Lonely

When a person dies we often feel afraid and lonely. Write down or draw a picture about these feelings.

_____

_____

Talk about why you are afraid and lonely.
Many people have these feelings and this is OK.

# Dreams

Have you had a dream about dying, or about _____?
*name*

Take this time to write about a dream
or draw a picture.

# Life Changes

Ways my life is different since _____ died.
*name*

_____

_____

_____

_____

Draw a picture of how your life has changed.

22

# Self-Care Maze

It is important to take care of yourself. These are some things to do that can make you feel better. Find your way through the maze.

Start here

Finish

call a friend

hug someone

rollerskate

do art work

bake cookies

give yourself a treat

listen to music

hug a toy

play outside

rest awhile

23

# My Letter

Write a letter to _____

*name*

You may write anything you feel like sharing.

Dear _____

_____

_____

_____

_____

_____

_____

_____

*your name* _____

You may want to write other letters later.

# Celebrating Life

Ask an adult to help you find ways to celebrate or honor this person's life. I will celebrate _____'s life by . . .
<br>*name*

_____

_____

_____ would feel proud of me because _____
*name*

_____

_____

_____

List three or more things

You may use these pages as you wish.

# Special Times

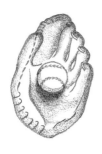

26

# Special Trips or Events

# Courage

I am a child of courage

I shared my feelings

I made a special Memory Book

The love and the keepsake

Will be there for me always